ROYAL
ACADEMY
OF ARTS
SKETCHBOOK

EBURY PRESS STATIONERY

FIRST PUBLISHED IN 1992 BY
EBURY PRESS STATIONERY
AN IMPRINT OF THE RANDOM CENTURY GROUP
RANDOM CENTURY HOUSE,
20 VAUXHALL BRIDGE ROAD,
LONDON SW1V 2SA
COPYRIGHT © RANDOM CENTURY GROUP 1992
ILLUSTRATIONS © PHILIP SUTTON RA 1992

SET IN ERHARDT
BY ⚓ TEK ART LTD, CROYDON SURREY

PRINTED IN ITALY

DESIGNED BY PETER BENNETT

ISBN 0 09 175 287 6

COVER ILLUSTRATION:
Philip Sutton RA, Houses of Parliament

SKETCHBOOK

SKETCHBOOK

SKETCHBOOK

SKETCHBOOK

SKETCHBOOK

SKETCHBOOK

SKETCHBOOK

SKETCHBOOK

SKETCHBOOK

SKETCHBOOK

SKETCHBOOK

SKETCHBOOK

SKETCHBOOK

SKETCHBOOK

SKETCHBOOK

SKETCHBOOK

SKETCHBOOK

SKETCHBOOK

SKETCHBOOK

SKETCHBOOK

SKETCHBOOK

SKETCHBOOK

SKETCHBOOK

SKETCHBOOK

SKETCHBOOK

SKETCHBOOK

SKETCHBOOK

SKETCHBOOK

SKETCHBOOK

SKETCHBOOK

SKETCHBOOK

SKETCHBOOK

SKETCHBOOK

SKETCHBOOK

SKETCHBOOK

SKETCHBOOK

SKETCHBOOK

SKETCHBOOK

SKETCHBOOK

SKETCHBOOK

SKETCHBOOK

SKETCHBOOK

SKETCHBOOK

SKETCHBOOK

SKETCHBOOK

SKETCHBOOK

SKETCHBOOK

SKETCHBOOK

SKETCHBOOK

SKETCHBOOK

SKETCHBOOK

SKETCHBOOK

SKETCHBOOK